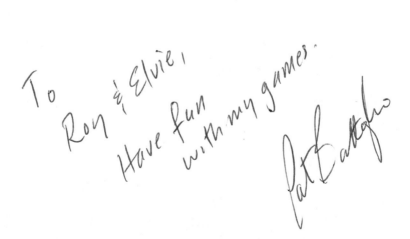

Are You Smart, or What?

A Bizarre Book of Games & Fun for Everyone

by
Pat Battaglia

To
Roy & Elvie,
Have fun
with my games.
Pat Battaglia

Are You Smart, or What?
A Bizarre Book of Games & Fun for Everyone
by Pat Battaglia

Publisher's Cataloging-in-Publication
(Provided by Quality Books, Inc.)

Battaglia, Pasqual J.
Are you smart, or what? : a bizarre book of games & fun for everyone / by Pat Battaglia. -- 1st ed.
p. cm.
LCCN: 2001086999
ISBN: 0-9708253-0-7

1. Word games. I. Title.

GV1507.W8B38 2001 793.734
QBI01-200315

Published by
International Puzzle Features
4507 Panther Place, Charlotte, NC 28269
(704) 921-1818
www.CleverPuzzles.com

Printed in the United States of America

Cover design and illustration by J. Pittman

First edition

Second Printing

GIFT PRESENTATION

This copy of **Are You Smart, or What?**
is given to ______________________
from the good-hearted soul known as

____
for the following occasion and/or reason(s):

- ☐ Your birthday
- ☐ Your graduation
- ☐ Your convalescence
- ☐ Christmas
- ☐ Special occasion (specify)

  ____

- ☐ Just for the fun of it
- ☐ Because you're so smart
- ☐ To find out if you're smart, or what

Also by **Pat Battaglia**

BOOKS

So You Think You're Smart:
150 Fun and Challenging Brain Teasers

If You're So Smart...

SYNDICATED NEWSPAPER COLUMN

If You're So Smart...

CONTRIBUTORS

The following people contributed puzzles that are included in this book. Each person was awarded $5 and a complimentary copy of **Are You Smart, or What?**

Florence Aaseng, McIntosh, MN

Rosemarie Goltz, Kenmore, NY

Leonard Gordon, Tucson, AZ

Patrick Jones, Powder Springs, GA

Mike Marcoe, Madison, WI

V. McIntosh, New York, NY

Jason Palazzo, Niagara Falls, NY

Dr. John Raymonda, Los Cruces, NM

YOU CAN BE FAMOUS, TOO

To get your name in print send your puzzle contribution(s) to

International Puzzle Features
4507 Panther Place
Charlotte, NC 28269

or submit on-line at www.CleverPuzzles.com

Contributors of puzzles chosen for publication will receive:

(1) their name in my next book and/or my **If You're So Smart...** syndicated newspaper puzzle column
(2) $5 for each puzzle chosen
(3) a complimentary autographed copy of my next book.

Only contributions selected for publication can be acknowledged.

ACKNOWLEDGMENTS

Many people deserve recognition for helping make this book possible. First and foremost is my wife Maralee. She has given me moral support, endured my constant requests to review my work, and has proofread virtually every puzzle that I have ever devised. Thank you, my love.

Thanks also go to Frank Mariani for the illustrations that he provided.

Finally, a thank you is extended to all the readers of my **If You're So Smart...** newspaper column from which many of the word games in this book were derived. Their interest as well as their contributions have helped provide me with the incentive to stretch my imagination to continuously develop new and entertaining puzzles.

CONTENTS

1 MENTAL WARM-UPS

Your **UPSET** quotient (Understanding Puzzles, Solving Effort & Thinking) follows Section 1.

2 MENTAL WORKOUTS

Your **MISERY** quotient (Mental Imagery of Solutions & Explanations with Regard to Yourself) follows Section 2.

3 MENTAL MIGRAINES

Your **ANGUISH** quotient (Agony 'N Grief in Understanding, Interpreting & Solving Handily) follows Section 3.

HANG ON A MINUTE

Everything about this book is unusual.

Let's start with the puzzles. You will find they're fun to work on. They're concise and uncomplicated so anyone can enjoy them. Some you may not solve, or at least not right away. But when the answers do dawn on you or you read them, you'll be amazed how easy and clever they were.

Some hints are provided (printed upside-down) as an incentive not to give up.

Many puzzles consist of a listing of numbered clues. An answer is associated with each clue. For these types of puzzles the degree of difficulty generally increases, the last one being the most challenging. So, if you solve the first few, don't get too confident. Wait until you've solved them all before thinking you're hot stuff.

The presentation of the answers is unique. The answer to each puzzle can be read on the *same page* as the statement of the puzzle. But the answer is not printed on that page. Sound like a contradiction? It isn't. Let me explain.

The answer to each puzzle is located within the outlined area following each puzzle. It is read by turning the book upside-down, facing the reverse side of the page to a light source and *looking through* the page. The answer revealed in this way is actually printed on the reverse side of the page that you will be reading. That's why you need a light source - to see *through* the page.

Why did I go through such an elaborate means of presenting the answers? Because with my scheme you can read the answer you want when you want it and *only* that answer. You completely avoid the aggravation of searching in the back of the book and seeing unwanted answers of puzzles that you haven't even tried yet. Besides, I wanted to create an extra special book that you will enjoy and remember for a long time.

Finally, I've included a means for scoring your solving ability that I think you'll find amusing. After you've checked your answer with mine, mark the appropriate square in the shaded area below each puzzle. Then, after you have finished a section, add your individual scores and enter the total on the tally sheet at the end of that section. What follows is a playful evaluation of your brain power.

Enough said. Now get going, enjoy my book and find out if you're smart, or what!

P. B.

Section 1

MENTAL WARM-UPS

Your **UPSET** quotient
(**U**nderstanding **P**uzzles,
Solving **E**ffort & **T**hinking)
follows Section 1.

ALL IN THE FAMILY

Tommy's mother has three children represented by the coins below. The first child is named Penny. The second is named Nicole. What is the name of the third child?

HINT: *Reread the puzzle. If the answer still doesn't dawn on you, read it again.*

ANSWER: Turn this page upside-down and look *through* the outlined portion into a light source.

Scoring points for your **UPSET** quotient (check one)

☐ My answer checks. I'm cool. (3 pts.)

☐ My answer's wrong. I goofed up. (0 pts.)

1. Sue 2. Art 3. Rob 4. Mike 5. Jim 6. Harry
7. Rod 8. Homer 9. Grace 10. Gail

WHAT'S MY LINE

Below is a list of ten occupations. Determine the name or nickname that sounds like a word whose meaning is associated with each occupation.

Example: banker **Answer**: Bill

1. lawyer
2. illustrator
3. thief
4. disk jockey
5. athletic teacher
6. barber
7. fisherman
8. baseball player
9. nun
10. meteorologist

Tommy's mother's third child is named Tommy.

Scoring points for your **UPSET** quotient (check one)

☐ I got all 10. (3 pts.) ☐ I got 7-9 right. (2 pts.)

☐ I got 3-6 right. (1 pt.) ☐ I've got to get going. (0 pts.)

ANSWER: Turn this page upside-down and look *through* the outlined portion into a light source.

SAY AGAIN

The wording of five well-known sayings has been changed to obscure their recognition. Identify the sayings.

Example: Frenzied activity generates worthless matter.
Answer: Haste makes waste.

1. It is impossible to evaluate published matter by recognition of the material enclosing such matter.
2. That quality appealing to the senses extends as far as the epidermis layer.
3. The commodity used as a medium of exchange is to be positioned at one's oral orifice.
4. Performed activity verbally communicates at an audible level substantially more intense than the individual sounds of a language.

ANSWER: Turn this page upside-down and look *through* the outlined portion into a light source.

Scoring points for your **UPSET** quotient (check one)

☐ I got all 4. (3 pts.) ☐ I got 2-3 right. (2 pts.)
☐ I got 1 right. (1 pt.) ☐ I've gotta get a better vocabulary. (0 pts.)

1. paralyze (pair of lies) 2. margarine (Marge you're in)
3. gladiator (glad he ate her) 4. moron (more on)

DOUBLE TALK

Complete each sentence by adding the proper word corresponding to each clue. Each word is completely unrelated to the sentence but sounds like the word(s) that fit into context.

Example: She went to the bank and asked for ____ .
Clue: by yourself
Answer: alone (sounds like "a loan.")

1. The two boys were spanked for telling their father a ____ .
   Clue: inability to move
2. The teacher found out that Marge played hooky and said, "____ deep trouble."
   Clue: substitute dairy product
3. The cannibal was unashamed and said he was ____ .
   Clue: Colosseum fighter
4. The TV anchorman mentioned a news story and said, "____ that later in the newscast."
   Clue: stupid person

1. You can't judge a book by its cover. 2. Beauty is only skin deep. 3. Put your money where your mouth is. 4. Actions speak louder than words.

Scoring points for your **UPSET** quotient (check one)

☐ I got all 4. (3 pts.) ☐ I got 2-3 right. (2 pts.)
☐ I got 1 right. (1 pt.) ☐ I got the example. (0 pts.)

ANSWER: Turn this page upside-down and look *through* the outlined portion into a light source.

CRAZY CLUES

What country is suggested by each of the following clues?

Example: a space shuttle **Answer**: Colombia

1. an animal
2. a prepared food
3. famished
4. dinnerware
5. a lubricant
6. an explosive shell

ANSWER: Turn this page upside-down and look *through* the outlined portion into a light source.

Scoring points for your **UPSET** quotient (check one)

☐ I got all 6. (3 pts.) ☐ I got 4-5 right. (2 pts.)

☐ I got 2-3 right. (1 pt.) ☐ I've got to learn geography. (0 pts.)

ALL AT ONCE

What two-letter word added after each of the ten letters below will spell a three-letter word?

b c e f h m p r s v

HINT: *The answer is at your fingertips.*

1. Turkey 2. Chile 3. Hungary 4. China 5. Greece 6. Grenada

Scoring points for your **UPSET** quotient (check one)

☐ My answer checks. I'm cool. (3 pts.)

☐ My answer's wrong. I goofed up. (0 pts.)

ANSWER: Turn this page upside-down and look *through* the outlined portion into a light source.

THREE'S COMPANY

Corresponding to each clue is a six-letter word. Three of the six letters in each word are the same. Identify each six-letter word.

Example: tell secrets **Answer**: tattle

1. fright
2. laugh
3. a condiment
4. a reflector
5. an animal sound
6. doll
7. a class of animals
8. buy back
9. enclosed gas
10. airy

ANSWER: Turn this page upside-down and look *through* the outlined portion into a light source.

Scoring points for your **UPSET** quotient (check one)

☐ I got all 10. (3 pts.) ☐ I got 7-9 right. (2 pts.)
☐ I got 3-6 right. (1 pt.) ☐ I'm a pour speller. (0 pts.)

1. rooms 2. times 3. ball 4. watch 5. over 6. board
7. drop 8. wise 9. green 10. ward 11. off 12. side

A COMMON PROBLEM

Determine the word that can be combined with each of the two words given below to form two compound words.

Example: mail ______ car
Answer: box (mailbox, boxcar)

1. dark _______ mate
2. day _______ table
3. foot _______ room
4. stop _______ dog
5. left _______ coat
6. key _______ walk
7. rain _______ out
8. clock _______ crack
9. winter _______ house
10. for _______ robe
11. lay _______ spring
12. way _______ ways

Scoring points for your **UPSET** quotient (check one)

☐ I got all 12. (3 pts.)
☐ I got 8-11 right. (2 pts.)
☐ I got 4-7 right. (1 pt.)
☐ I've got a com-pounding headache. (0 pts.)

ANSWER: Turn this page upside-down and look *through* the outlined portion into a light source.

STATE YOUR PROBLEM

Determine the states of the United States that have an initial sound that is pronounced the same as a letter of the alphabet.

HINT: *There are seven states.*

ANSWER: Turn this page upside-down and look *through* the outlined portion into a light source.

Scoring points for your **UPSET** quotient (check one)

☐ I got all 7. (3 pts.) ☐ I got 5-6 right. (2 pts.)
☐ I got 3-4 right. (1 pt.) ☐ I got the "O" states. (0 pts.)

Sign in an optometrist's office: This is the site for sore eyes

A PHONY MESSAGE

The letters associated with the numbers on a telephone are:

2	3	4	5	6	7	8	9
ABC	DEF	GHI	JKL	MNO	PRS	TUV	WXY

Place the appropriate letter corresponding to each number given below to complete the quip.

Sign in an optometrist's office:

8 4 4 7   4 7   8 4 3   7 4 8 3

3 6 7   7 6 7 3   3 9 3 7

Scoring points for your **UPSET** quotient (check one)

☐ My answer checks. I'm cool. (3 pts.)

☐ My answer's wrong. I goofed up. (0 pts.)

ANSWER: Turn this page upside-down and look *through* the outlined portion into a light source.

SPELLBOUND

Complete the spelling of six hyphenated words. A clue to each word is given in parentheses.

Example: __ ce-co __ __ (32°F) **Answer**: ice-cold

1. __ __ __ ss-ex __ __ __ __ __ (questioning)
2. __ __ rt-ch __ __ __ (very inexpensive)
3. __ __ lf-ma __ __ (sign of mourning)
4. __ ar-fe __ __ __ __ __ (hard to believe)
5. __ __ en-ai __ (outdoor)
6. __ __ ng-wi __ __ __ __ (talkative)

ANSWER: Turn this page upside-down and look *through* the outlined portion into a light source.

Scoring points for your **UPSET** quotient (check one)

☐ I got all 6. (3 pts.) ☐ I got 4-5 right. (2 pts.)
☐ I got 2-3 right. (1 pt.) ☐ I got 1 right. (0 pts.)

A3, B6, C10, D1, E7, F8, G9, H2, I4, J5

JUST FOR KICKS

Match each word in the left-hand column with a silly definition in the right-hand column.

A. arbitrator	1. a clumsy ophthalmologist
B. avoidable	2. what trees do in spring
C. burglarize	3. quitting Arby's to work at McDonald's
D. eyedropper	4. what to do to relax your wife
E. heroes	5. what a seafood store owner does
F. baloney	6. what a bullfighter does
G. pharmacist	7. what a guy in a boat does
H. relief	8. where some hemlines fall
I. rubberneck	9. a helper on a farm
J. selfish	10. what a crook sees with

1. cross-examine 2. dirt-cheap 3. half-mast
4. far-fetched 5. open-air 6. long-winded

Scoring points for your **UPSET** quotient (check one)

☐ I got all 10. (3 pts.) ☐ I got 7-9 right. (2 pts.)
☐ I got 3-6 right. (1 pt.) ☐ I was varicose to doing better. (0 pts.)

ANSWER: Turn this page upside-down and look *through* the outlined portion into a light source.

SWEET HUNTING

Identify the name of each candy bar suggested by the clue.

Example: outer space **Answer**: Milky Way

1. a planet
2. a street
3. miniature hills
4. a sound
5. compensation time
6. plump
7. a bird
8. suppressed laughs

ANSWER: Turn this page upside-down and look *through* the outlined portion into a light source.

Scoring points for your **UPSET** quotient (check one)

☐ I got all 8. (3 pts.) ☐ I got 5-7 right. (2 pts.)
☐ I got 2-4 right. (1 pt.) ☐ I'm not a sweet person. (0 pts.)

1. blackboard 2. black eye 3. black tie 4. blackmail 5. black magic
6. blacksmith 7. black belt 8. black widow 9. blackjack 10. black hole

BLACKOUT

Determine the word or two-word phrase beginning with the word "black" that is associated with each hint.

Example: road **Answer**: blacktop

1. classroom
2. shiner
3. formal
4. a felony
5. voodoo
6. occupation
7. self-defense
8. poisonous
9. twenty-one
10. nothingness

Scoring points for your **UPSET** quotient (check one)

☐ I got all 10. (3 pts.) ☐ I got 7-9 right. (2 pts.)
☐ I got 3-6 right. (1 pt.) ☐ I blacked out. (0 pts.)

ANSWER: Turn this page upside-down and look *through* the outlined portion into a light source.

ALIAS ALERT

Match the personality in the left-hand column with the birth or "real" name from the right-hand column by placing the appropriate letter in the space provided.

____ 1. Superman	A. Leslie King, Jr.
____ 2. Elton John	B. Vlad Tepes
____ 3. Pope John Paul II	C. Clark Kent
____ 4. President Gerald Ford	D. Ehrich Weiss
____ 5. John Wayne	E. Israel Baline
____ 6. Mother Teresa	F. Reginald Dwight
____ 7. Muhammed Ali	G. Marion Morrison
____ 8. Harry Houdini	H. Karol Josef Wojtyla
____ 9. Dracula	I. Agnes Bojaxhiu
____10. Irving Berlin	J. Cassius Clay

ANSWER: Turn this page upside-down and look *through* the outlined portion into a light source.

Scoring points for your **UPSET** quotient (check one)

☐ I got all 10. (3 pts.) ☐ I got 7-9 right. (2 pts.)
☐ I got 3-6 right. (1 pt.) ☐ I got Superman's name. (0 pts.)

1. trash, rash, ash 2. chair, hair, air 3. strip, trip, rip 4. strain, train, rain 5. smart, mart, art 6. spout, pout, out 7. charm, harm, arm 8. scream, cream, ream 9. price, rice, ice 10. clone, lone, one

TRIPLE THREAT

Determine three words, corresponding to the three clues, with spellings that only differ by a beginning letter.

Example: curtain, a crime, has long arms
Answer: drape, rape, ape

1. garbage, a skin irritation, a residue
2. a body rest, comes in strands, a gas
3. a narrow piece, journey, tear
4. stress, a vehicle, comes in drops
5. brilliant, a shopping center, a nickname
6. the pouring edge, sulk, removed
7. a trinket, damage, an extremity
8. yell, full of cholesterol, 500
9. what you pay, a grain, it's cold
10. identical, by itself, single

1C, 2E, 3H, 4A, 5G, 6I, 7J, 8D, 9B, 10E

Scoring points for your **UPSET** quotient (check one)

☐ I got all 10. (3 pts.) ☐ I got 7-9 right. (2 pts.)
☐ I got 3-6 right. (1 pt.) ☐ I'm clueless. (0 pts.)

ANSWER: Turn this page upside-down and look *through* the outlined portion into a light source.

SENTENCE PENANCE

Determine a word that completes each of the following six sentences. All six words rhyme.

1. The children were taught not to _____ .
2. The meal gave him _____ .
3. It shines like polished _____ .
4. She was asked to _____ the cookies.
5. The toy broke like it was _____ .
6. She hurried so she wouldn't miss _____ .

ANSWER: Turn this page upside-down and look *through* the outlined portion into a light source.

Scoring points for your **UPSET** quotient (check one)

☐ My answer checks. I'm cool. (3 pts.)

☐ My answer's wrong. I goofed up. (0 pts.)

1. single, 2. strike 3. steal 4. batter 5. bull pen
6. bat 7. homer 8. base 9. ball 10. pitch

GRAND SLAM

Determine the word or phrase associated with the game of baseball that is suggested by each clue.

Example: a container **Answer**: pitcher

1. unmarried
2. worker's protest
3. a crime
4. mixture for baking
5. fenced area
6. a mammal
7. a male name
8. bottom support
9. lavish event
10. tone

1. sass 2. gas 3. brass 4. bass 5. glass 6. class

Scoring points for your **UPSET** quotient (check one)

☐ I got all 10. (3 pts.) ☐ I got 7-9 right. (2 pts.)
☐ I got 3-6 right. (1 pt.) ☐ I struck out. (0 pts.)

ANSWER: Turn this page upside-down and look *through* the outlined portion into a light source.

MONKEY BUSINESS

Fill in the blanks in each sentence with a word that is pronounced the same (but spelled differently) as the name of a creature.

Example: A lot of shouting can make you _____ .
Answer: hoarse (pronounced the same as "horse")

1. His _____ came to the family reunion.
2. He was only 30 but had very little _____ .
3. She cried when her pet died because it was _____ to her.
4. He went on a hike _____ from the waist up.
5. The infant would often _____ all night.
6. Everyone ignored him because he was a _____ .

ANSWER: Turn this page upside-down and look *through* the outlined portion into a light source.

Scoring points for your **UPSET** quotient (check one)

☐ I got all 6. (3 pts.)
☐ I got 4-5 right. (2 pts.)
☐ I got 2-3 right. (1 pt.)
☐ I've got to quit horsing around. (0 pts.)

UNCHANGED EXCHANGE

What one word can be substituted for all six underlined words?

1. He had to return home immediately after work.
2. They would smuggle guns across the border.
3. He could manage his business very well.
4. She had a lot of good luck at the casino.
5. He knew how to operate the machine.
6. She let the water flow for ten minutes.

1. aunt (ant) 2. hair (hare) 3. dear (deer)
4. pare (pear) 5. wail (whale) 6. bore (boar)

Scoring points for your **UPSET** quotient (check one)

☐ My answer checks. I'm cool. (3 pts.)

☐ My answer's wrong. I goofed up. (0 pts.)

ANSWER: Turn this page upside-down and look *through* the outlined portion into a light source.

RHYME & REASON

Determine a set of rhyming words associated with each pair of clues.

Example: a toy, tell secrets **Answer**: rattle, tattle

1. currency, humorous
2. a boat, big
3. for sure, drapery
4. clue, a flavor
5. royal house, hard skin
6. slender, a weapon
7. country, controlled supply
8. stable, hazard
9. royal chair, section
10. cultivated ground, forgive
11. a relative, twelve
12. brain, fruit covering

ANSWER: Turn this page upside-down and look *through* the outlined portion into a light source.

Scoring points for your **UPSET** quotient (check one)

☐ I got all 12. (3 pts.) ☐ I got 8-11 right. (2 pts.)
☐ I got 4-7 right. (1 pt.) ☐ I got rhymed out. (0 pts.)

CITY SLICKER

In what order are the following U.S. cities listed?

Los Angeles
Miami
Honolulu
Chicago
Minneapolis
Buffalo
Philadelphia

1. money, funny 2. barge, large 3. certain, curtain 4. hint, mint
5. palace, callus 6. narrow, arrow 7. nation, ration 8. manger, danger
9. throne, zone 10. garden, pardon 11. cousin, dozen 12. mind, rind

Scoring points for your **UPSET** quotient (check one)

☐ My answer checks. I'm cool. (3 pts.)

☐ My answer's wrong. I goofed up. (0 pts.)

ANSWER: Turn this page upside-down and look *through* the outlined portion into a light source.

BEWITCHING

Given below are six well-known phrases with wording that has been changed to obscure their recognition. Each phrase refers to a superstition. Identify the phrases.

Example: Strike a fibrous material with a sharp blow.
Answer: Knock on wood.

1. causing the fracture of a brittle reflective surface
2. taking the extremity of an appendage of a burrowing animal with you
3. to move on foot beneath a climbing device
4. displaying a quadruped's hoofwear on a vertical surface
5. your intended walkway being traversed by a feline of the darkest color
6. to come upon a plant with foliage that is abnormal

ANSWER: Turn this page upside-down and look *through* the outlined portion into a light source.

Scoring points for your **UPSET** quotient (check one)

☐ I got all 6. (3 pts.) ☐ I got 4-5 right. (2 pts.)
☐ I got 2-3 right. (1 pt.) ☐ I've got no luck. (0 pts.)

1. arms 2. legs 3. eye 4. mouth 5. tongue or heel
6. teeth 7. head 8. neck 9. pupils 10. jaw

PARTLY HUMAN

The name of a portion of each of the ten items given below is also the name of a part of the human body. Name the ten parts.

Example: clock **Answer**: face

1. chair
2. table
3. tornado
4. river
5. shoe
6. saw
7. nail
8. bottle
9. school
10. vise

1. breaking a mirror 2. carrying a rabbit's foot
3. walking under a ladder 4. hanging a horseshoe
5. a black cat crosses your path 6. finding a four-leaf clover

Scoring points for your **UPSET** quotient (check one)

☐ I got all 10. (3 pts.) ☐ I got 7-9 right. (2 pts.)
☐ I got 3-6 right. (1 pt.) ☐ I've got weak brain cells. (0 pts.)

ANSWER: Turn this page upside-down and look *through* the outlined portion into a light source.

CREATURE FEATURE

Determine the name of the animal that rhymes with the last word of the following phrases.

Example: See you later, _____ . **Answer**: alligator

1. What's new, _____ .
2. See you soon, _____ .
3. You're no dope, _____ .
4. Drop me a line, _____ .
5. What's all the fuss, _____ .
6. Let's not tarry, _____ .
7. I'm the boss, _____ .

ANSWER: Turn this page upside-down and look *through* the outlined portion into a light source.

Scoring points for your **UPSET** quotient (check one)

☐ I got all 7. (3 pts.) ☐ I got 4-6 right. (2 pts.)
☐ I got 2-3 right. (1 pt.) ☐ I'm in the dark, aardvark. (0 pts.)

1. David & Goliath 2. Johnson & Johnson 3. Smith & Wesson 4. Lewis & Clark 5. Batman & Robin 6. Black & Decker 7. Bonnie & Clyde 8. Barnes & Noble 9. Ben & Jerry 10. Dun & Bradstreet

PAIR OFF

The first letters of the names of well-known pairs of people, both real and fictional, are given below. A hint to each pair is also given. Determine the name pairs.

Example: H ____ & G ____ fairy tale
Answer: Hansel & Gretel

1. D ____	& G ____	Biblical opponents
2. J ____	& J ____	baby products
3. S ____	& W ____	weapons
4. L ____	& C ____	explorers
5. B ____	& R ____	superheroes
6. B ____	& D ____	tools
7. B ____	& C ____	outlaws
8. B ____	& N ____	books
9. B ____	& J ____	treat
10. D ____	& B ____	financial

1. kangaroo or caribou 2. raccoon or baboon 3. antelope
4. porcupine 5. rhinoceros 6. dromedary 7. albatross

Scoring points for your **UPSET** quotient (check one)

☐ I got all 10. (3 pts.) ☐ I got 7-9 right. (2 pts.)
☐ I got 3-6 right. (1 pt.) ☐ I got tired & quit. (0 pts.)

ANSWER: Turn this page upside-down and look *through* the outlined portion into a light source.

UNFORGETTABLE

Add the missing letter and determine the word that can be spelled by starting at the appropriate letter and moving in the proper direction (clockwise or counterclockwise) around the circle.

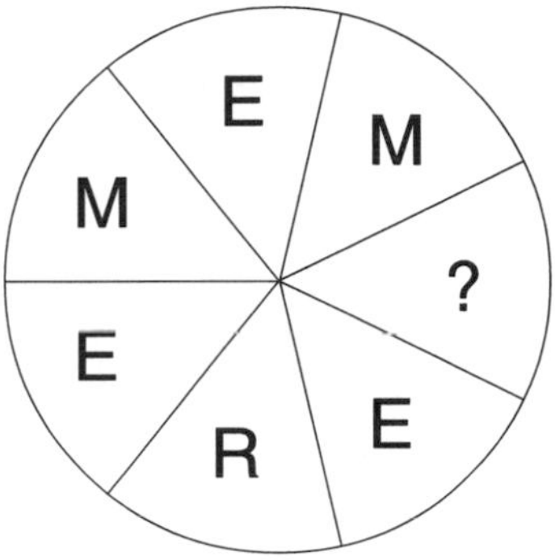

ANSWER: Turn this page upside-down and look *through* the outlined portion into a light source.

Scoring points for your **UPSET** quotient (check one)

☐ My answer checks. I'm cool. (3 pts.)

☐ My answer's wrong. I goofed up. (0 pts.)

1. constant 2. conscious 3. concur 4. consume
5. converse 6. concept 7. contest 8. conclude
9. confine 10. confess 11. connect 12. conquer

A CON JOB

Each of the following 12 words suggests another word that begins with "con." Determine the words.

Example: prisoner **Answer**: convict

1. unchanging
2. aware
3. agree
4. eat
5. talk
6. idea
7. tournament
8. finish
9. limit
10. admit
11. fasten
12. defeat

The word is remember.

Scoring points for your **UPSET** quotient (check one)

☐ I got all 12. (3 pts.) ☐ I got 8-11 right. (2 pts.)
☐ I got 4-7 right. (1 pt.) ☐ I got con-fused. (0 pts.)

ANSWER: Turn this page upside-down and look *through* the outlined portion into a light source.

FIRST NAME, LAST WORD

Complete each sentence with a person's name or nickname that fits in context.

Example: Her favorite school subject was ____ .
Answer: art

1. Silent Night was her favorite Christmas ____ .
2. The tacos were made using spices and ground ____ .
3. He was looking in his car's trunk for the ____ .
4. A woodpecker must have a tough ____ .
5. Her ice skating performance was filled with beauty & ____ .
6. She was afraid to enter the house because it was built on a ____ .
7. When jumping over the fence his pants were torn by a ____ .
8. She flavored her food with a particular ____ .

ANSWER: Turn this page upside-down and look *through* the outlined portion into a light source.

Scoring points for your **UPSET** quotient (check one)

☐ I got all 8. (3 pts.) ☐ I got 5-7 right. (2 pts.)
☐ I got 2-4 right. (1 pt.) ☐ I doug for answers in vain. (0 pts.)

THE END

Determine the word ending with "end" that corresponds to each clue.

Example: cause hurt feelings **Answer**: offend

1. pal
2. fix
3. loan
4. act
5. plan
6. be present
7. advise
8. change
9. hang
10. mix

Scoring points for your **UPSET** quotient (check one)

☐ I got all 10. (3 pts.) ☐ I got 7-9 right. (2 pts.)
☐ I got 3-6 right. (1 pt.) ☐ Me no compre'end. (0 pts.)

ANSWER: Turn this page upside-down and look *through* the outlined portion into a light source.

Your **UPSET** quotient (**U**nderstanding **P**uzzles, **S**olving **E**ffort & **T**hinking) for Section 1

Procedure for determining your **UPSET** quotient:

1. Add your scores for the puzzles in Section 1.
2. Record this total in the space below.
3. Check the box corresponding to your total score.
4. Read your **UPSET** quotient results opposite the box checked.

My total score for Section 1 is ____ points.

UPSET quotient results

Total Score	Your UPSET Level	Current Evaluation	Section 2 Projected Result
75-90	upset-free	You should be proud of yourself. You're terrific!	You'll do excellently.
60-74	mild	You should be pleased. Good going.	You'll do well.
45-59	aching	Try harder. Don't give up so easily.	Make up your mind to do better.
30-44	acute	Were you sleeping in school? Get with it!	You're headed for big trouble.
15-29	agonizing	You're score is pathetic! Pray for enlightenment.	Don't even try it.
0-14	excruciating	Do you even have a pulse? Call 911 now!	Get plenty of bed rest instead.

Section 2, coming up.
Shift your brain into high gear.

Section 2

MENTAL WORKOUTS

Your **MISERY** quotient
(**M**ental **I**magery of
Solutions & **E**xplanations
with **R**egard to **Y**ourself)
follows Section 2.

A MENTAL BLOCK

The two blocks below are marked identically. What side is opposite the side marked with a "D?"

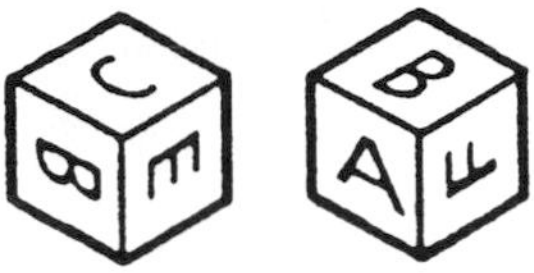

HINT: *Be alert and concentrate your reasoning around the proper side.*

ANSWER: Turn this page upside-down and look *through* the outlined portion into a light source.

Scoring points for your **MISERY** quotient (check one)

☐ I solved it. I'm brilliant. (3 pts.) ☐ I understood the puzzle. (1 pt.)
☐ I didn't get it. (0 pts.)

One of the most frequently used alphabet characters, the letter "e," does not appear in the paragraph.

A PARTICULARLY PERPLEXING PARAGRAPH

This is an unusual paragraph. It has a trait not found in many paragraphs of this many words. Can you find out what it is? It's not as hard as you might think. Just look and study. I know you can do it. Good luck!

HINT: *This puzzle is not extremely difficult nor can it be done with ease.*

Scoring points for your **MISERY** quotient (check one)

☐ I solved it. I'm brilliant. (3 pts.)   ☐ I eat bran & veggies. (1 pt.)

☐ I didn't get it. (0 pts.)

ANSWER: Turn this page upside-down and look *through* the outlined portion into a light source.

SOUNDS FISHY

Complete each sentence with the name of a fish that sounds similar to a word(s) that fit into context.

> **Example**: If you're deaf, you've lost your ____ .
> **Answer**: herring (hearing)

1. ____ Monroe was a famous movie star.
2. He went bungy jumping just for the ____ .
3. Yogi ____ been a star on any baseball team.
4. The ____ left his wife with three small children.
5. The fresh baked bread ____ good and tasted great.
6. The ad jingle was a ____ person would easily remember.
7. The contented cat would often ____ moments notice.

ANSWER: Turn this page upside-down and look *through* the outlined portion into a light source.

Scoring points for your **MISERY** quotient (check one)

☐ I got 'em all perfect. (3 pts.) ☐ I solved 4-6 correctly. (2 pts.)
☐ I got 2-3 right. (1 pt.) ☐ I tried anyway. (0 pts.)

All are names of U.S. presidents: 1. Lincoln (link + kin)
2. Grant (grr. + aunt) 3. Nixon (nix + in) 4. Johnson (john + son)
5. Truman (true + man) 6. Harding (hard + ding)

EXECUTIVE PRONOUNCEMENT

Determine the last names of six people by pronouncing the word suggested by each clue. All people are deceased and have been nationally known.

Example: which person + 4th alphabetical character + leg joint
Answer: Houdini (who + D + knee)

1. loop of chain + relative
2. tiger sound + a female relative
3. slang for disapproval + not out
4. bathroom + male offspring
5. valid + adult male
6. difficult + partial doorbell sound

HINT: *All people share a common trait.*

1. marlin (Marilyn) 2. halibut (hell of it) 3. barracuda (Berra could of)
4. eel (heel) 5. smelt (smelled) 6. tuna (tune a) 7. piranha (purr on a)

Scoring points for your **MISERY** quotient (check one)

☐ I got 'em all perfect. (3 pts.) ☐ I solved 4-5 correctly. (2 pts.)
☐ I got 2-3 right. (1 pt.) ☐ I tried anyway. (0 pts.)

ANSWER: Turn this page upside-down and look *through* the outlined portion into a light source.

DOUBLE UP

Determine the word, suggested by each clue, that either begins or ends in a double letter.

Example: African animal **Answer**: aardvark

1. a state
2. glove
3. cost or charge
4. animal haven
5. estimate
6. South American animal
7. insect sound
8. exude or flow slowly
9. earth bulge
10. mysterious

ANSWER: Turn this page upside-down and look *through* the outlined portion into a light source.

Scoring points for your **MISERY** quotient (check one)

☐ I got 'em all perfect. (3 pts.) ☐ I solved 7-9 correctly. (2 pts.)

☐ I got 3-6 right. (1 pt.) ☐ I tried anyway. (0 pts.)

There are forty-two eyes pictures. Did you remember that each card has two faces pictured on it?

AN EYE OPENER

Of all the face cards in a standard deck of playing cards, only the jack of hearts, jack of spades and king of diamonds have one eye pictured. All other face cards have a view where both eyes of each character are pictured. How many eyes are pictured in a standard 52-card deck?

HINT: *If you think the answer is 21, you're wrong!*

1. Hawaii or Tennessee 2. mitt 3. fee 4. zoo
5. guess 6. llama 7. buzz 8. ooze 9. hill 10. eerie

Scoring points for your **MISERY** quotient (check one)

☐ I solved it. I'm brilliant. (3 pts.) ☐ I change my underwear daily. (1 pt.)

☐ I didn't get it. (0 pts.)

ANSWER: Turn this page upside-down and look *through* the outlined portion into a light source.

JUST HORSING AROUND

Corresponding to each of the ten clues given below is a well-known phrase or saying that has the name of a creature in it. Determine the ten phrases and sayings.

Example: ultra slow **Answer**: snail's pace

1. faking death
2. perceive a spy
3. tattletale
4. obstinate
5. serious conversation
6. create trouble
7. source of information
8. reveal problems
9. unrestricted
10. unleash

ANSWER: Turn this page upside-down and look *through* the outlined portion into a light source.

Scoring points for your **MISERY** quotient (check one)

☐ I got 'em all perfect. (3 pts.) ☐ I solved 7-9 correctly. (2 pts.)
☐ I got 3-6 right. (1 pt.) ☐ I tried anyway. (0 pts.)

The android will walk because it has been programmed to act only with four-letter words.

ROBOT REASONING

A certain android eats cake but not pie, drinks milk but not water, reads a book but not a magazine, sits on a sofa but not in a chair. Will it walk or run and why?

Scoring points for your **MISERY** quotient (check one)

☐ I solved it. I'm brilliant. (3 pts.) ☐ I use my car's turn signals. (1 pt.)

☐ I didn't get it. (0 pts.)

ANSWER: Turn this page upside-down and look *through* the outlined portion into a light source.

YOUR TREAT

Would it cost more for you to take ten people to one football game or four people to each of five baseball games? Or would it cost the same? Each football ticket costs twice as much as each baseball ticket.

HINT: *If you determined that the costs are the same, you forgot something.*

ANSWER: Turn this page upside-down and look *through* the outlined portion into a light source.

Scoring points for your **MISERY** quotient (check one)

☐ I solved it. I'm brilliant. (3 pts.) ☐ I always buckle up. (1 pt.)

☐ I didn't get it. (0 pts.)

1. soft drink 2. cold turkey 3. big deal 4. world class
5. money hungry 6. easy street 7. rain check 8. blind date
9. flat broke 10. wet blanket 11. white wash 12. think tank

FRAZE DAZE

Determine the two words suggested by each clue that will form well-known two-word phrases.

Example: deceased, exhausted **Answer**: dead tired

1. not firm, swallow
2. frigid, gobble, gobble
3. huge, distribute
4. earth, category
5. currency, famished
6. simple, thoroughfare
7. precipitation, money order
8. sightless, a fruit
9. deflated, smashed
10. soggy, bedding
11. a color, launder
12. meditate, a large container

Did you forget yourself in determining ticket costs? You will need 11 football tickets or 25 baseball tickets. The baseball tickets would cost more.

Scoring points for your **MISERY** quotient (check one)

☐ I got 'em all perfect. (3 pts.) ☐ I solved 8-11 correctly. (2 pts.)

☐ I got 4-7 right. (1 pt.) ☐ I tried anyway. (0 pts.)

ANSWER: Turn this page upside-down and look *through* the outlined portion into a light source.

SMALL TALK

Mr. Adams met an old friend of his that he hadn't seen in many years. After exchanging pleasantries, they began to tell each other personal news. The friend said "I was married ten years ago to someone you never knew. This is my daughter here with me." Mr. Adams said hello to the little girl and asked her what her name was. The girl replied "I have the same name as my mother." Mr. Adams then responded, "Then your name must be Rose."

How did Mr. Adams know the little girl's name?

ANSWER: Turn this page upside-down and look *through* the outlined portion into a light source.

Scoring points for your **MISERY** quotient (check one)

☐ I solved it. I'm brilliant. (3 pts.) ☐ I'm a veteran. (1 pt.)

☐ I didn't get it. (0 pts.)

1. sweet sixteen 2. to the bitter end 3. sourpuss 4. with a grain of salt
5. sour grapes 6. sweet dreams 7. salt away 8. bitter pill to swallow.

A TASTEFUL TASK

Determine the saying described by each clue. Each saying has the name of a taste in it.

Example: deserving of one's wages **Answer**: earn your salt

1. a special age
2. conclusion of an unpleasant situation
3. a grouchy disposition
4. making allowances for the source of information
5. pretended disdain for something one doesn't have
6. have an enjoyable sleep
7. to keep in reserve
8. a disagreeable situation one must accept

HINT: *There are only four tastes: bitter, salt, sweet and sour.*

Scoring points for your **MISERY** quotient (check one)

☐ I got 'em all perfect. (3 pts.) ☐ I solved 5-7 correctly. (2 pts.)

☐ I got 2-4 right. (1 pt.) ☐ I tried anyway. (0 pts.)

ANSWER: Turn this page upside-down and look *through* the outlined portion into a light source.

FERRET OUT ANSWERS

Complete each sentence by adding the name of an animal.

Example: The computer was idle because the ____ was broken.
Answer: mouse

1. He was so tall he had to ____ going through the doorway.
2. He hit the ball hard and broke the ____ .
3. A ____ was used to move the steel beam into place.
4. He drank the shot with one big ____ .
5. She was a ____ when she didn't get her own way.
6. They called him a ____ because he was short for his age.
7. He would always ____ on his companions when they were in trouble.
8. He was a ____ , always clinging to another for personal gain.

ANSWER: Turn this page upside-down and look *through* the outlined portion into a light source.

Scoring points for your **MISERY** quotient (check one)

☐ I got 'em all perfect. (3 pts.) ☐ I solved 5-7 correctly. (2 pts.)
☐ I got 2-4 right. (1 pt.) ☐ I tried anyway. (0 pts.)

1. eye 2. tot 3. noon 4. madam 5. toot 6. deed
7. level 8. rotor 9. kayak 10. reviver

PALINDROMIC PONDERING

Determine the word corresponding to each clue that is spelled the same backward and forward.

Example: a female name **Answer**: Hannah

1. a body part
2. small child
3. a time of day
4. a women's title
5. a vehicle sound
6. a legal document
7. flat
8. helicopter blades
9. a water craft
10. resuscitator

Scoring points for your **MISERY** quotient (check one)

☐ I got 'em all perfect. (3 pts.) ☐ I solved 7-9 correctly. (2 pts.)

☐ I got 3-6 right. (1 pt.) ☐ I tried anyway. (0 pts.)

ANSWER: Turn this page upside-down and look *through* the outlined portion into a light source.

WHAT'S THE DIFFERENCE?

Which abbreviation is different from the rest and why?

wt.	wk.
oz.	Lt.
Mr.	jr.
ft.	ht.
St.	vs.

ANSWER: Turn this page upside-down and look *through* the outlined portion into a light source.

Scoring points for your **MISERY** quotient (check one)

☐ I solved it. I'm brilliant. (3 pts.) ☐ I buy Girl Scout cookies. (1 pt.)

☐ I didn't get it. (0 pts.)

1. polar molar 2. tot cot 3. bright light 4. jail mail
5. dandy brandy 6. hefty lefty 7. dwarf wharf
8. mole hole 9. chip dip 10. ecstatic fanatic

RHYME TIME

Determine a two-word rhyme similar in meaning to each of the ten phrases.

Example: unhappy father **Answer**: sad dad

1. white bear's tooth
2. child bed
3. intense illumination
4. prison correspondence
5. fine liqueur
6. rotund southpaw
7. small dock
8. animal burrow
9. snack sauce
10. very happy extremist

Oz (ounce) is the only abbreviation that is not formed by the first and last letters of the abbreviated word.

Scoring points for your **MISERY** quotient (check one)

☐ I got 'em all perfect. (3 pts.) ☐ I solved 7-9 correctly. (2 pts.)

☐ I got 3-6 right. (1 pt.) ☐ I tried anyway. (0 pts.)

ANSWER: Turn this page upside-down and look *through* the outlined portion into a light source.

HAVE A BALL

In what order are the following sports listed?

golf
tennis
baseball
softball
bowling
soccer
basketball

ANSWER: Turn this page upside-down and look *through* the outlined portion into a light source.

Scoring points for your **MISERY** quotient (check one)

☐ I solved it. I'm brilliant. (3 pts.) ☐ I donate to charities. (1 pt.)

☐ I didn't get it. (0 pts.)

1. elephant 2. eulogy 3. embassy 4. extend 5. baby 6. element
7. enema 8. ecstasy 9. excuse 10. euphoric 11. exceed 12. envious

D + SIFE + ER

Decipher the following to reveal 12 words.

1. LFN + t
2. U + la + G
3. M + ba + C
4. X + 10 + d
5. b + AB
6. LMN + t
7. NM + a
8. X + ta + C
9. XQ + s
10. U + 4 + ic
11. XC + d
12. NV + us

The sports are listed in increasing order of the size of the ball used.

Scoring points for your **MISERY** quotient (check one)

☐ I got 'em all perfect. (3 pts.) ☐ I solved 8-11 correctly. (2 pts.)

☐ I got 4-7 right. (1 pt.) ☐ I tried anyway. (0 pts.)

ANSWER: Turn this page upside-down and look *through* the outlined portion into a light source.

FALLOUT

Spell a sentence starting with the bold square and moving to adjacent squares one at a time going right, left, up and down, but not diagonally. Use each of the 25 letter squares once.

N	E	G	R	E
T	E	R	**E**	V
R	E	S	E	L
S	E	D	N	D
S	H	E	E	E

HINT: *Many people get acquainted with this fact during the Christmas season.*

ANSWER: Turn this page upside-down and look *through* the outlined portion into a light source.

Scoring points for your **MISERY** quotient (check one)

☐ I solved it. I'm brilliant. (3 pts.) ☐ I vote in every election. (1 pt.)

☐ I didn't get it. (0 pts.)

1. room, broom 2. all, ball 3. beat, eat 4. race, brace
5. each, beach 6. read, bread 7. blame, lame 8. bright, right

BE SHARP

Complete each sentence by adding two words. The two words are spelled identically except that the letter "B" is added to the beginning of one of the words.

Example: God ___ the ___ fortunate among us.
Answer: bless, less

1. She swept the ___ with a ___ .
2. They ___ went to the ___ park to watch the game.
3. You can't ___ a restaurant that serves all you can ___ .
4. The injured athlete ran the ___ wearing a ___ .
5. ___ vacationer got sunburned at the ___ .
6. She ___ the recipe on how to bake ___ .
7. A skiing accident was to ___ for her ___ leg.
8. The ___ sun shown ___ through the curtains.

Scoring points for your **MISERY** quotient (check one)

☐ I got 'em all perfect. (3 pts.) ☐ I solved 5-7 correctly. (2 pts.)
☐ I got 2-4 right. (1 pt.) ☐ I tried anyway. (0 pts.)

ANSWER: Turn this page upside-down and look *through* the outlined portion into a light source.

CAR TROUBLE

Name the make of the automobile that is suggested by each of the following clues. (Remember, it is the make, not the model of the car that is to be determined.)

Example: ringed planet **Answer**: Saturn

1. a bird
2. hot heavenly body
3. a USA state capital
4. an animal
5. shallow crossing
6. boundless
7. evade
8. weep

ANSWER: Turn this page upside-down and look *through* the outlined portion into a light source.

Scoring points for your **MISERY** quotient (check one)

☐ I got 'em all perfect. (3 pts.) ☐ I solved 5-7 correctly. (2 pts.)

☐ I got 2-4 right. (1 pt.) ☐ I tried anyway. (0 pts.)

1. peach (beach) 2. fig (big) 3. date (hate) 4. grape (drape)
5. lime (dime) 6. cherry (very) 7. plum (glum) 8. raisin (brazen)

A FRUITFUL CHALLENGE

Determine the name of the fruit that rhymes with the word that is suggested by each clue.

Example: extremely seldom
Answer: pear (rhymes with rare)

1. sandy shore
2. large
3. intense dislike
4. curtain
5. a coin
6. extremely
7. sad
8. bold

Scoring points for your **MISERY** quotient (check one)

☐ I got 'em all perfect. (3 pts.)
☐ I solved 5-7 correctly. (2 pts.)
☐ I got 2-4 right. (1 pt.)
☐ I tried anyway. (0 pts.)

ANSWER: Turn this page upside-down and look *through* the outlined portion into a light source.

MISSING LINK

The same letter is missing 15 times in the string of letters below. Determine this letter, insert it in the appropriate places and separate the words formed to make a sentence.

n r d v r k ' s m m m l t h t h s s h r p c l w s n d t t c k s n t s.

ANSWER: Turn this page upside-down and look *through* the outlined portion into a light source.

Scoring points for your **MISERY** quotient (check one)

☐ I solved it. I'm brilliant. (3 pts.) ☐ I believe in recycling. (1 pt.)

☐ I didn't get it. (0 pts.)

Rehearse is the only word where the "re" is not a prefix meaning to repeat the root word.

REFLECT ON IT

Which word is different from the rest and why?

rewind
reassure
redirect
rehearse
reelect
revisit
rearrange
reprint

An aardvark's a mammal that has sharp claws and attacks ants.

Scoring points for your **MISERY** quotient (check one)
☐ I solved it. I'm brilliant. (3 pts.) ☐ I return library books on time. (1 pt.)
☐ I didn't get it. (0 pts.)

ANSWER: Turn this page upside-down and look *through* the outlined portion into a light source.

CHILD'S PLAY

Given below are phrases that capture the main theme of ten well-known nursery rhymes. Identify the nursery rhymes.

Example: man critical from fall from perch
Answer: Humpty-Dumpty

1. owner shadowed by pet
2. girl frightened out of eating
3. woman and pet without food
4. concussion caused by fall
5. lost sheep to return
6. udderly amazing feat
7. king: alive with pleasure
8. boy forces affection on girls
9. neglect of duties allows animals to stray
10. wool supply donated

ANSWER: Turn this page upside-down and look *through* the outlined portion into a light source.

Scoring points for your **MISERY** quotient (check one)

☐ I got 'em all perfect. (3 pts.) ☐ I solved 7-9 correctly. (2 pts.)
☐ I got 3-6 right. (1 pt.) ☐ I tried anyway. (0 pts.)

COMPOUND INTEREST

Two clues to each of ten well-known compound words are given below. The first clue is a hint to the first portion of the compound word and the second is a hint to the second portion. Determine the ten compound words.

Example: body part, illuminate **Answer**: headlight

1. skillet, dessert
2. lawn, pogo stick
3. dairy product, insect
4. ocean, dandelion
5. adult male, gentle
6. musical instrument, twig
7. resting place, extend
8. mind, blizzard
9. fracture, quick
10. fun activity, soil

1. Mary Had a Little Lamb 2. Little Miss Muffet 3. Old Mother Hubbard
4. Jack and Jill 5. Little Bo Peep 6. Hey Diddle Diddle 7. Old King Cole
8. Georgey Porgey 9. Little Boy Blue 10. Ba Ba Black Sheep

Scoring points for your **MISERY** quotient (check one)

☐ I got 'em all perfect. (3 pts.) ☐ I solved 7-9 correctly. (2 pts.)

☐ I got 3-6 right. (1 pt.) ☐ I tried anyway. (0 pts.)

ANSWER: Turn this page upside-down and look *through* the outlined portion into a light source.

PLAY THE GAME

Substitute each underlined clue with a word that will form a well-known saying.

Example: fracture the frozen solid
Answer: break the ice

1. strike the street
2. transfer the dollar
3. big stone the watercraft
4. scrape the exterior
5. punch the accumulated money
6. rotate the dining furniture
7. beyond the mound
8. 12" the check
9. go higher the stream
10. clothe the slacks

ANSWER: Turn this page upside-down and look *through* the outlined portion into a light source.

Scoring points for your **MISERY** quotient (check one)

☐ I got 'em all perfect. (3 pts.) ☐ I solved 7-9 correctly. (2 pts.)
☐ I got 3-6 right. (1 pt.) ☐ I tried anyway. (0 pts.)

A bazooka is worth four points. The number of vowels in each word determines the worth.

A POINTED QUESTION

In a video game, the scoring is as follows:

- Tanks and ships are worth 1 point each.
- Jeeps and planes are worth 2 points each.
- Missiles and soldiers are worth 3 points each.

How many points is a bazooka worth and why?

1. hit the road 2. pass the buck 3. rock the boat 4. scratch the surface 5. hit the jackpot 6. turn the tables 7. over the hill 8. foot the bill 9. up the creek 10. wear the pants

Scoring points for your **MISERY** quotient (check one)

☐ I solved it. I'm brilliant. (3 pts.) ☐ I donate blood. (1 pt.)

☐ I didn't get it. (0 pts.)

ANSWER: Turn this page upside-down and look *through* the outlined portion into a light source.

MATRIX MAGIC

Place the word suggested by each clue in the appropriate horizontal and vertical spaces in the framework.

1. a container
2. connect
3. an anesthetic
4. part of a play
5. a number

	1	2	3	4	5
1					
2					
3					
4					
5					

ANSWER: Turn this page upside-down and look *through* the outlined portion into a light source.

Scoring points for your **MISERY** quotient (check one)

☐ I got 'em all perfect. (3 pts.) ☐ I solved 3-4 correctly. (2 pts.)

☐ I got 1-2 right. (1 pt.) ☐ I tried anyway. (0 pts.)

THE BEGINNING OF THE END

Identify the word corresponding to each clue that begins and ends with the same letter.

Example: antique **Answer**: classic

1. expired
2. entice
3. joke
4. flat
5. type of sign
6. permitted
7. most
8. a spiritualist
9. consumable
10. twist or curl

Scoring points for your **MISERY** quotient (check one)

☐ I got 'em all perfect. (3 pts.) ☐ I solved 7-9 correctly. (2 pts.)

☐ I got 3-6 right. (1 pt.) ☐ I tried anyway. (0 pts.)

ANSWER: Turn this page upside-down and look *through* the outlined portion into a light source.

Your **MISERY** quotient (**M**ental **I**magery of **S**olutions & **E**xplanations with **R**egard to **Y**ourself) for Section 2

Procedure for determining your **MISERY** quotient:

1. Add your scores for the puzzles in Section 2.
2. Record this total in the space below.
3. Check the box corresponding to your total score.
4. Read your **MISERY** quotient results opposite the box checked.

My total score for Section 2 is ____ points.

MISERY quotient results

Total Score	Your MISERY Level	Your Evaluation
75-90	nonexistent	Your mental imagery is unexcelled. You're kinda like a genius!
60-74	pretty darn low	Your mental imagery is highly commendable. Keep it up.
45-59	getting nasty	Your mental imagery is getting hazy, or are you just lazy?
30-44	really nasty	Your mental imagery may be good but not about puzzle solutions.
15-29	pretty darn high	Your mental imagery stinks. Please don't try Section 3.
0-14	horrendous	You likely don't have any mental images. You're kinda like a mental case.

Section 3 is dead ahead.
This is for the gold. Go for it!

Section 3

MENTAL MIGRAINES

Your **ANGUISH** quotient
(**A**gony **'N** **G**rief in
Understanding, **I**nterpreting
& **S**olving **H**andily)
follows Section 3.

GOING IN CIRCLES

Each of the letter circles below represent a seven-letter word. Each word can be spelled by starting at the appropriate letter and moving clockwise or counterclockwise around the circle. Identify the words.

Example:

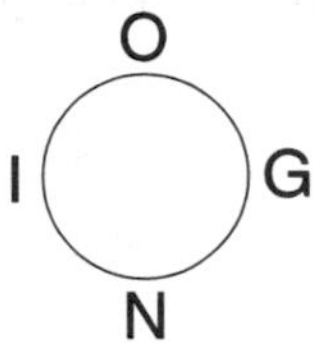

Answer: INGOING

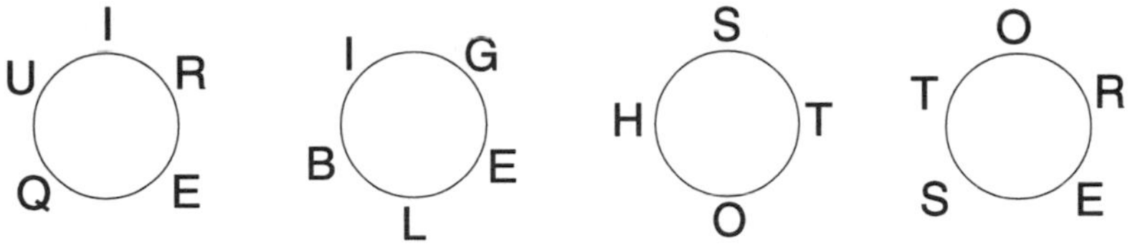

ANSWER: Turn this page upside-down and look *through* the outlined portion into a light source.

Scoring points for your **ANGUISH** quotient (check one)

☐ All 4 correct. I'm terrific! (3 pts.) ☐ 3 correct. I'm good. (2 pts.)

☐ 2 correct. I'm so-so. (1 pt.) ☐ 0-1 correct. I'm dense. (0 pts.)

A grapefruit from the box labeled "pink and white" must be either all pink or all white. If the grapefruit is found to be white, put the "white" label on that box and switch the remaining two labels. Do similarly if the grapefruit is pink.

LABEL LOGIC

Three boxes of grapefruit are incorrectly labeled. The labels read “white”, “pink” and “pink and white.” Visual identification can only be made by cutting the grapefruit and noting the pink or white color. By taking a single grapefruit from one of the boxes and cutting it open, determine how to switch labels to correctly identify the boxes.

Scoring points for your **ANGUISH** quotient (check one)

☐ I solved it. Boy, am I ever smart! (3 pts.)

☐ I screwed up. (0 pts.)

ANSWER: Turn this page upside-down and look *through* the outlined portion into a light source.

FLOWER POWER

Each clue below refers to a word that rhymes with a name of a common flower. Determine the name of each flower.

Example: facial organ **Answer**: rose (rhymes with nose)

1. opposite of ambitious
2. nonsensical
3. duplicate
4. a cause of disease
5. converge into clarity
6. holiday
7. skull

ANSWER: Turn this page upside-down and look *through* thc outlined portion into a light source.

Scoring points for your **ANGUISH** quotient (check one)

☐ All 7 correct. I'm terrific! (3 pts.) ☐ 4-6 correct. I'm good. (2 pts.)

☐ 2-3 correct. I'm so-so. (1 pt.) ☐ 0-1 correct. I'm slow. (0 pts.)

On Monday the man brings seven dirty shirts to the laundry, picks up seven clean shirts and wears one shirt - a total of fifteen.

CLEANING CONFUSION

A man wears a clean shirt every day. He brings the shirts he has worn to the laundry every Monday afternoon and picks up the cleaned shirts exactly one week later on the following Monday afternoon. How many shirts must the man own to ensure that he can wear a clean shirt every day?

HINT: *Eight is not enough.*

1. daisy (lazy) 2. lily (silly) 3. poppy (copy) 4. iris (virus)
5. crocus (locus) 6. carnation (vacation) 7. geranium (cranium)

Scoring points for your **ANGUISH** quotient (check one)

☐ I solved it. I am one cool dude/dudess! (3 pts.)

☐ I screwed up. (0 pts.)

ANSWER: Turn this page upside-down and look *through* the outlined portion into a light source.

ACCENTUATING CIRCUMSTANCES

Determine the one word that can be inserted in both spaces in each sentence. The meaning and pronunciation of the word in the two locations are different.

Example: The supervisor was asked to ____ the ____ to the retiree.
Answer: present (first meaning is "to give", the second is "a gift.")

1. She shed a ____ over the ____ in her expensive evening gown.
2. A ____ is a ____ portion of an entire year.
3. He ____ a rope around his leg to stop the ____ from bleeding
4. It was easy to ____ class because student ____ was excellent.
5. The farmer was able to ____ better ____ than anyone else.
6. The ____ ____ to the rescue of its hatched babies.
7. He was in the ____ helping to carry a statue that seemed to be made of ____ .
8. The ____ of ____ means not to speak.

ANSWER: Turn this page upside-down and look *through* the outlined portion into a light source.

Scoring points for your **ANGUISH** quotient (check one)

☐ All 8 correct. I'm terrific! (3 pts.) ☐ 5-7 correct. I'm good. (2 pts.)
☐ 2-4 correct. I'm so-so. (1 pt.) ☐ 0-1 correct. I'm dull. (0 pts.)

The sequence is 8, 5, 4, 9, 1, 7, 6, 3, and 2.
The numbers are in alphabetical order.

SEQUENTIAL MATH

Complete the following sequence by placing an appropriate digit in the proper spaces.

8, 5, 4, 9, ___ , 7, ___ , ___ , 2

1. tear 2. minute 3. wound 4. conduct
5. produce 6. dove 7. lead 8. converse

Scoring points for your **ANGUISH** quotient (check one)

☐ I solved it. Nothing escapes me! (3 pts.)

☐ I screwed up. (0 pts.)

ANSWER: Turn this page upside-down and look *through* the outlined portion into a light source.

TOUGH TO FIGURE

The names in each column share a peculiar characteristic. What are the two characteristics?

BOB	ALLAN
GUS	KEVIN
RUSS	TIM
DOUG	KEN
BUD	MIKE

HINT: *The name JOHN has both characteristics.*

ANSWER: Turn this page upside-down and look *through* the outlined portion into a light source.

Scoring points for your **ANGUISH** quotient (check one)

☐ I solved it. My reasoning is flawless! (3 pts.)

☐ I screwed up. (0 pts.)

LOOKING FOUR-WORDS

Each pair of hints below relates to a pair of four-letter words. The two words are composed of the same letters. Only the order of the letters is changed to form two different words. Determine the words.

Example: hill of sand, unclothed **Answer**; dune, nude

1. food from animals, domesticated
2. fibber, guard or barrier
3. slight smile, circular band
4. large stores, intelligent
5. smell, entrance barrier
6. uninteresting, nightwear
7. deserve, close to
8. a fruit, harvest
9. layer, make weary
10. leg wear, footwear

Scoring points for your **ANGUISH** quotient (check one)

☐ All 10 correct. I'm terrific! (3 pts.) ☐ 7-9 correct. I'm good. (2 pts.)
☐ 3-6 correct. I'm so-so. (1 pt.) ☐ 0-2 correct. I'm thick. (0 pts.)

ANSWER: Turn this page upside-down and look *through* the outlined portion into a light source.

IN PLAIN SIGHT

What is the next symbol in the following sequence?

 ?

HINT: *Concentrate on one-half of the puzzle.*

ANSWER: Turn this page upside-down and look *through* the outlined portion into a light source.

Scoring points for your **ANGUISH** quotient (check one)

☐ I solved it. I'm great - and good looking, too! (3 pts.)

☐ I screwed up. (0 pts.)

1. touch 2. sew 3. wool 4. sour
5. bury 6. pint 7. mood 8. fever

NO RHYME OR REASON

For each pair of words determine a word that is spelled with a different beginning letter but does not rhyme with the words in the pair.

Example: bugged, mugged **Answer**: rugged

1. couch, pouch
2. new, few
3. fool, tool
4. four, pour
5. fury, jury
6. hint, mint
7. wood, hood
8. never, sever

The sequence is the first letters of the days of the week. Each symbol consists of the letter turned sideways and placed next to its mirror image. Therefore, the next symbol is ⊔⊔ .

Scoring points for your **ANGUISH** quotient (check one)

☐ All 8 correct. I'm terrific! (3 pts.) ☐ 5-7 correct. I'm good. (2 pts.)
☐ 2-4 correct. I'm so-so. (1 pt.) ☐ 0-1 correct. I'm hopeless. (0 pts.)

ANSWER: Turn this page upside-down and look *through* the outlined portion into a light source.

AT WITS END

Fill in the missing letters to spell the word that corresponds to the clue given. Each word ends with the name of an animal. The last letter of each word is given to help you.

Example: _ _ x container **Answer**: box (Ox is the animal.)

1. _ _ _ _ _ _ _ _ _ n uprising
2. _ _ _ _ _ _ _ _ t political
3. _ _ _ _ e portion
4. _ _ _ _ e form
5. _ _ _ _ _ _ _ n pagan
6. _ _ _ _ _ _ _ _ _ t bears blame
7. _ _ _ _ _ _ _ m illustration, figure
8. _ _ _ _ k boat

ANSWER: Turn this page upside-down and look *through* the outlined portion into a light source.

Scoring points for your **ANGUISH** quotient (check one)

☐ All 8 correct. I'm terrific! (3 pts.) ☐ 5-7 correct. I'm good. (2 pts.)

☐ 2-4 correct. I'm so-so. (1 pt.) ☐ 0-1 correct. I'm terrible. (0 pts.)

1. BagDAD 2. LIVERpool 3. MANila 4. ANCHORage 5. Los ANGELes

6. BOMBay 7. BosTON 8. HaVANa 9. BudaPEST 10. ZuRICH

WHAT'S IN A NAME?

Given below is a clue followed by a country or state. Identify the city in the country or state that has a word within its spelling that is suggested by the clue.

Example: animal, Russia **Answer**: MosCOW

1. father, Iraq
2. body organ, England
3. person, Philippines
4. ship equipment, Alaska
5. spirit, California
6. explosive, India
7. unit of weight, Massachusetts
8. vehicle, Cuba
9. annoy, Hungary
10. wealthy, Switzerland

Scoring points for your **ANGUISH** quotient (check one)

☐ All 10 correct. I'm terrific! (3 pts.) ☐ 7-9 correct. I'm good. (2 pts.)

☐ 3-6 correct. I'm so-so. (1 pt.) ☐ 0-2 correct. I'm awful. (0 pts.)

ANSWER: Turn this page upside-down and look *through* the outlined portion into a light source.

THE NAME GAME

Determine the name or nickname that rhymes with the word similar in meaning to each word or phrase.

Example: a threat to cause harm
Answer: Dennis (rhymes with menace)

1. eternal happiness
2. a play thing
3. to cry loudly
4. amusements or pastimes
5. vocal sounds
6. a ravine or canyon
7. skeleton material
8. hearing disorder
9. fake
10. stop
11. a recurring series of events
12. provides rotary motion

ANSWER: Turn this page upside-down and look *through* the outlined portion into a light source.

Scoring points for your **ANGUISH** quotient (check one)

☐ All 12 correct. I'm terrific! (3 pts.) ☐ 8-11 correct. I'm good. (2 pts.)
☐ 4-7 correct. I'm so-so. (1 pt.) ☐ 0-3 correct. I'm pitiful. (0 pts.)

DIFFERENT STROKES

One of the following words is different from the rest. Which one and why?

contest	entrance
mark	desert
wind	record
bass	console
project	content

1. Kevin (heaven) 2. Roy (toy) 3. Paul (bawl) 4. James (games)
5. Joyce (voice) 6. George (gorge) 7. Joan (bone) 8. Jeff (deaf)
9. Tony (phony) 10. Walt (halt) 11. Michael (cycle) 12. Frank (crank)

Scoring points for your **ANGUISH** quotient (check one)

☐ I solved it. I can solve anything! (3 pts.)

☐ I screwed up. (0 pts.)

ANSWER: Turn this page upside-down and look *through* the outlined portion into a light source.

PRESIDENTIAL MATERIAL

Rearrange the letters in each word or phrase to spell the last name of an United States president.

Example: a range **Answer**: Reagan

1. tracer
2. domains
3. hubs
4. I creep
5. saw nothing
6. film role
7. I see her now
8. glide far
9. vote loser
10. no more
11. my nickel
12. brave nun

ANSWER: Turn this page upside-down and look *through* the outlined portion into a light source.

Scoring points for your **ANGUISH** quotient (check one)

☐ All 12 correct. I'm terrific! (3 pts.) ☐ 8-11 correct. I'm good. (2 pts.)
☐ 4-7 correct. I'm so-so. (1 pt.) ☐ 0-3 correct. I'm dreadful. (0 pts.)

The letters of each word are in alphabetical order.

A COMMON QUESTION

Each of the following eight words have the same unusual quality. What is it?

empty
almost
first
chop
fort
dirty
adopt
begin

HINT: *This puzzle is made to order.*

Scoring points for your **ANGUISH** quotient (check one)

☐ I solved it. No doubt about it, I'm incredible! (3 pts.)

☐ I screwed up. (0 pts.)

ANSWER: Turn this page upside-down and look *through* the outlined portion into a light source.

A FULL HOUSE

A particular object is associated with each category given below. The four objects are common to a single item. Determine the four objects and the item.

garden tools
body organs
gems
weapons

ANSWER: Turn this page upside-down and look *through* the outlined portion into a light source.

Scoring points for your **ANGUISH** quotient (check one)

☐ I solved it. I'm unstoppable! (3 pts.)

☐ I screwed up. (0 pts.)

1. Sue, use 2. Rose, sore 3. Leah, heal
4. Ron, nor 5. Lois, soil 6. Omar, roam

NAMELY ANAGRAMS

Complete each sentence by adding a person's name or nickname and another word spelled with the same letters as the name.

Example: ____ took ____ dancing lessons.
Answer: Pat took tap dancing lessons.

1. ____ would ____ her influence to obtain box seat tickets.
2. ____ had a ____ nose from constant sneezing.
3. ____ knew the incision would ____ quickly.
4. ____ liked neither asparagus ____ broccoli.
5. ____ loved to plant and work the ____ .
6. ____ enjoyed traveling and would ____ from town to town.

The objects are a spade, heart, diamond and club. All are common to a deck of cards.

Scoring points for your **ANGUISH** quotient (check one)

☐ All 6 correct. I'm terrific! (3 pts.) ☐ 4-5 correct. I'm good. (2 pts.)
☐ 2-3 correct. I'm so-so. (1 pt.) ☐ 0-1 correct. I'm pathetic. (0 pts.)

ANSWER: Turn this page upside-down and look *through* the outlined portion into a light source.

RIDDLE RATTLE

It can be short.
It can be long.
If you think it has weight,
You are definitely wrong!

It can't be heard.
It can be seen.
For heaven's sake,
What do I mean?

What is it?

ANSWER: Turn this page upside-down and look *through* the outlined portion into a light source.

Scoring points for your **ANGUISH** quotient (check one)

☐ I solved it. I admit it. I'm brilliant! (3 pts.)

☐ I screwed up. (0 pts.)

Mary is the banker. Diane is the truck driver. Paul is the mailman. Fred is the Editor. Ed is the Teacher.

OCCUPATIONAL HAZARD

From the facts given below, determine the occupation of each of the five people.

- The editor and Mary are honeymooning in Hawaii.
- The truck driver and mailman both have blue eyes.
- Diane and the banker are vegetarians.
- Fred has false teeth.
- Ed's sister-in-law is the banker.
- The teacher's wife has flaming red hair.
- Paul is a bachelor.

Scoring points for your **ANGUISH** quotient (check one)

☐ All 5 correct. I'm terrific! (3 pts.) ☐ 3-4 correct. I'm good. (2 pts.)
☐ 2 correct. I'm so-so. (1 pt.) ☐ 0-1 correct. I'm miserable. (0 pts.)

ANSWER: Turn this page upside-down and look *through* the outlined portion into a light source.

HODGE PODGE

The meanings of eight common two-word phrases are given below. The words of each phrase rhyme. Identify the phrases.

Example: dull minded **Answer**: nit wit

1. counterfeit
2. faithful
3. much too much
4. overweight
5. communication system
6. improper behavior
7. refers to trickery
8. offensive action
9. exodus of intelligent people
10. equal score
11. an ideal assemblage
12. details

ANSWER: Turn this page upside-down and look *through* the outlined portion into a light source.

Scoring points for your **ANGUISH** quotient (check one)

☐ All 12 correct. I'm terrific! (3 pts.) ☐ 8-11 correct. I'm good. (2 pts.)
☐ 4-7 correct. I'm so-so. (1 pt.) ☐ 0-3 correct. I'm impossible. (0 pts.)

1. faculty, family 2. rooster, roster 3. orange, range
4. heaven, haven 5. prosper, proper 6. pleasant, peasant
7. varnish, vanish 8. scary, scar 9. Irish, iris 10. covert, cover

IN A SPELL

Given below are ten pairs of clues. The first clue in each pair refers to a particular word. The second clue refers to a different word that is spelled the same as the first word except that one letter is removed. Determine the ten words.

Example: more distant, dad **Answer**: farther, father

1. school teachers, imperfect
2. farm animal, list of people
3. a fruit, stove
4. paradise, a safe place
5. financial success, appropriate
6. nice, serf
7. shellac, disappear
8. frightful, skin mark
9. a nationality, eye part
10. secret, wrongful desire

Scoring points for your **ANGUISH** quotient (check one)

☐ All 10 correct. I'm terrific! (3 pts.) ☐ 7-9 correct. I'm good. (2 pts.)

☐ 3-6 correct. I'm so-so. (1 pt.) ☐ 0-2 correct. I'm horrible. (0 pts.)

ANSWER: Turn this page upside-down and look *through* the outlined portion into a light source.

PECULIAR PROPERTY

Which word is different from the rest and why?

upholster
nephew
epitaph
phrase
graphic
prophesy

ANSWER: Turn this page upside-down and look *through* the outlined portion into a light source.

Scoring points for your **ANGUISH** quotient (check one)

☐ I solved it. I'm terrific and hardly ever conceited! (3 pts.)

☐ I screwed up. (0 pts.)

1. star, rats 2. live, evil 3. keep, peek 4. guns, snug
5. part, trap 6. reward, drawer 7. straw, warts
8. plug, gulp 9. tool, loot 10. ward, draw

TO AND FRO

Each pair of hints below relates to two words. One of the words is the other one spelled backwards. What are the ten word pairs?

Example: married, moisture **Answer**; wed, dew

1. light source, rodents
2. dwell, wicked
3. retain, sneaking look
4. weapons, tight fit
5. portion, catching device
6. prize, furniture compartment
7. drinking aid, skin blemishes
8. stopper, big swallow
9. implement, stolen goods
10. precinct, illustrate

Each word contains a "ph," and upholster is the only one where those letters are not pronounced like an "f."

Scoring points for your **ANGUISH** quotient (check one)

☐ All 10 correct. I'm terrific! (3 pts.) ☐ 7-9 correct. I'm good. (2 pts.)
☐ 3-6 correct. I'm so-so. (1 pt.) ☐ 0-2 correct. I'm appalling. (0 pts.)

ANSWER: Turn this page upside-down and look *through* the outlined portion into a light source.

EQUATION OCCASION

How can you correct the Roman Numeral equation given below without adding, removing, or repositioning any line(s)?

XI + I = X

HINT: *If you have difficulty, take a different view of the problem.*

ANSWER: Turn this page upside-down and look *through* the outlined portion into a light source.

Scoring points for your **ANGUISH** quotient (check one)

☐ I solved it. My ability is becoming legendary! (3 pts.)

☐ I screwed up. (0 pts.)

1. Mr., blister, sister 2. swallow, follow, hollow 3. ghost, roast, boast 4. fight, right, might 5. power, hour, sour 6. duck, truck, buck 7. mourn, horn, corn 8. pound, mound, round 9. royal, foil, soil 10. ditch, hitch, pitch

TRIPLE PLAY

Determine the rhyming words associated with each group of clues.

Example: sightless, intellect, good-hearted
Answer: blind, mind, kind

1. male title, skin swelling, a sibling
2. gulp, comes next, empty inside
3. spirit, cook in oven, brag
4. combat, correct, after dark
5. energy, a time period, a taste
6. a fowl, a vehicle, a deer
7. grieve, bugle, a grain
8. tied, raised earth, circular
9. imperial, work, dirt
10. trench, connect, throw

Turn the page upside-down and the equation becomes valid.

Scoring points for your **ANGUISH** quotient (check one)

☐ 10 correct. I'm terrific! (3 pts.) ☐ 7-9 correct. I'm good. (2 pts.)
☐ 3-6 correct. I'm so-so. (1 pt.) ☐ 0-2 correct. I'm horrendous. (0 pts.)

ANSWER: Turn this page upside-down and look *through* the outlined portion into a light source.

NOT TWO COMMON

What unusual trait do each of the following words have in common?

telephone
shorten
canine
height
feminine
overweight
often
throne

HINT: *Work hard and don't quit and you're sure to solve this puzzle in the end.*

ANSWER: Turn this page upside-down and look *through* the outlined portion into a light source.

Scoring points for your **ANGUISH** quotient (check one)

☐ I solved it. My mind is razor sharp! (3 pts.)

☐ I screwed up. (0 pts.)

If you get this you're pretty darn good.

UNCOMMON SENSE

Determine a word that rhymes with each word given below to make an intelligible sentence.

Whiff zoo bet kiss tour gritty yarn could.

Each word ends in the spelling of a number.

Scoring points for your **ANGUISH** quotient (check one)

☐ I solved it. Is there no limit to my ability?! (3 pts.)

☐ I screwed up. (0 pts.)

ANSWER: Turn this page upside-down and look *through* the outlined portion into a light source.

Your **ANGUISH** quotient (**A**gony '**N** **G**rief in **U**nderstanding, **I**nterpreting & **S**olving **H**andily) for Section 3

Procedure for determining your **ANGUISH** quotient:

1. Add your scores for the puzzles in Section 3.
2. Record this total in the space below.
3. Check the box corresponding to your total score.
4. Read your **ANGUISH** quotient results opposite the box checked.

My total score for Section 3 is ____ points.

ANGUISH quotient results

Total Score	Your ANGUISH Level	Your Evaluation
70-84	nil	You've worked like a demon, so please take to heart, The kudos you deserve, by golly you're smart!
55-69	insignificant	You've missed genius level by only a bit. It's very obvious you are quite a wit.
40-54	significant	Half the time you succeed, the other half you quit. You fall in the category of a half-wit.
25-39	excessive	Your understanding is often quite null. Guess, you might say, your mind is just dull.
11-24	extreme	Your answers are wrong. You just make no sense. The only conclusion is, boy are you dense!
0-10	overwhelming	I hate to tell you, this may come as a jolt. But, I must say, you've the mind of a dolt!

More Fun & Games!

12th printing

Supply is Limited. Order now.

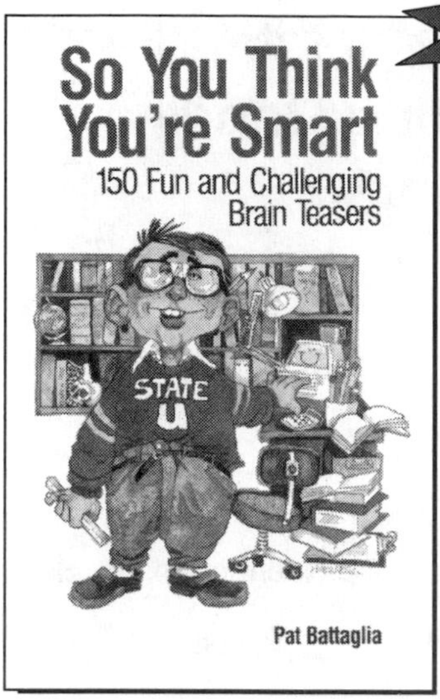

Have fun with Pat Battaglia's previous best selling book.

So You Think You're Smart is a delightful book of word games that the entire family can enjoy.

The games are only one of the fun features. All answers are encrypted! Each is given on the same page as the game, but is printed in a mirror image - and a special unbreakable mirror is provided with each book.

To Order:

☎ **TELEPHONE:** Call Toll-Free 1-866-FUN-1818 (386-1818)

ON-LINE: www.CleverPuzzles.com or www.Amazon.com

✉ **POSTAL:** Use an order form on the next page. ⇨ ⇨ ⇨ ⇨

Give Gifts of Fun

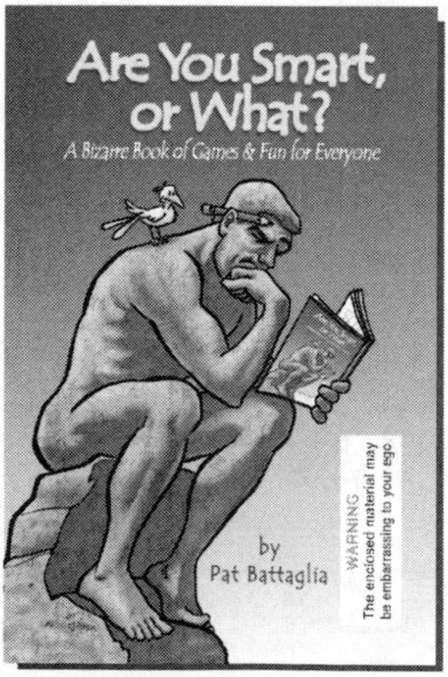

Are You Smart, or What?
is the perfect teasing gift for:

- birthdays
- Christmas
- graduations
- convalescents
- traveling
- parties
- vacations
- camping
- Mother's Day & Father's Day
- Boss's Day & Secretary's Day
- Valentine's Day
- just for fun on any day

Go to **www.CleverPuzzles.com** for special discounts on bulk copies for fund-raising, educational use, premiums, etc.

International Puzzle Features
4507 Panther Place, Charlotte, NC 28269

Please send copies of the following books. If I am not completely satisfied I will return them for a prompt refund, no questions asked.

______ Number of copies of **Are You Smart, or What?**
______ Number of copies of **So You Think You're Smart**
______ Total number of copies at $9.95 each .... $ ________

Shipping & Handling (total for all books ordered) .... $ 3.00

Sales tax, NC residents only, add $0.65 per book .... $ ________

Total amount of check or money order enclosed .... $ ________

Name ____

Address ____ Apt.# _____

City ___________________________ State ______ Zip _________

Make check or money order payable to International Puzzle Features

$AVE ON SHIPPING COST$
Buy multiple copies using the mail-in order form & save on shipping.

International Puzzle Features
4507 Panther Place, Charlotte, NC 28269

Please send copies of the following books. If I am not completely satisfied I will return them for a prompt refund, no questions asked.

______ Number of copies of **Are You Smart, or What?**
______ Number of copies of **So You Think You're Smart**
______ Total number of copies at $9.95 each .... $ ________

Shipping & Handling (total for all books ordered) .... $ 3.00

Sales tax, NC residents only, add $0.65 per book .... $ ________

Total amount of check or money order enclosed .... $ ________

Name ____

Address ____ Apt.# _____

City ___________________________ State ______ Zip _________

Make check or money order payable to International Puzzle Features

The End

So, are you smart, or what?